W.A. Mozart

CONCERTO for CLARINET

(K622)

Revised and Arranged for
B-flat Clarinet Solo with Piano Accompaniment
by
Simeon Bellison

CARL FISCHER®

Printed in the U. S. A.

W1668

ISBN 978-0-8258-0441-0

Sheet Music Edition
W1668

CONCERTO

for

CLARINET in Bb (original in A Major)

W. A. MOZART Op. 107, K. 622
Revised and Arranged by
Simeon Bellison

f
p
tr
cresc.
f
p
f
f

Solo
Solo
p
p
col voce
tr
f
f
f
1
f
p
p
p
cresc.
f
espr.
mf
dolce.
fz
p
pp

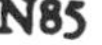

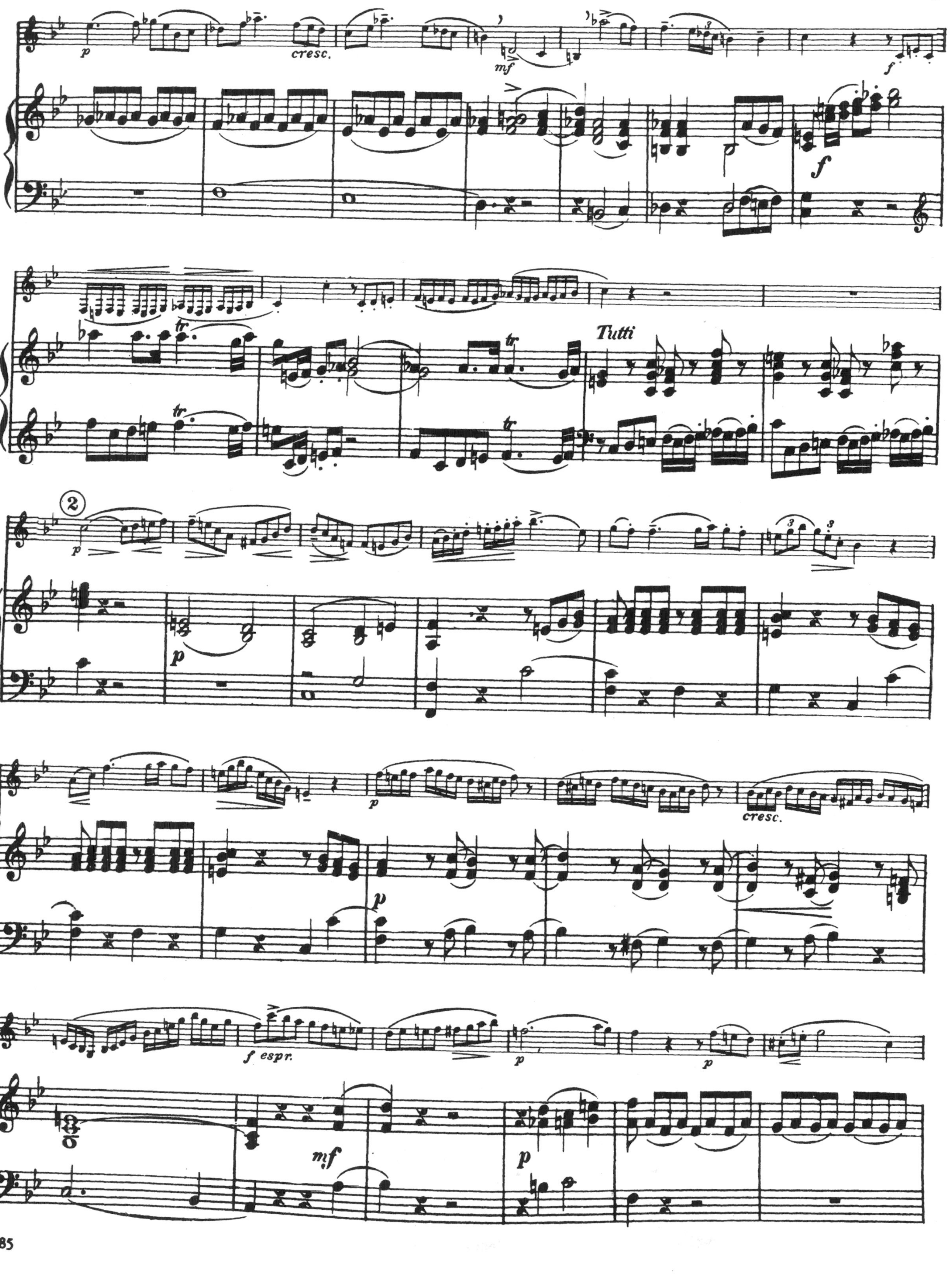
p
cresc.
mf
f
Tutti
tr
2
espr.
mf
p
f

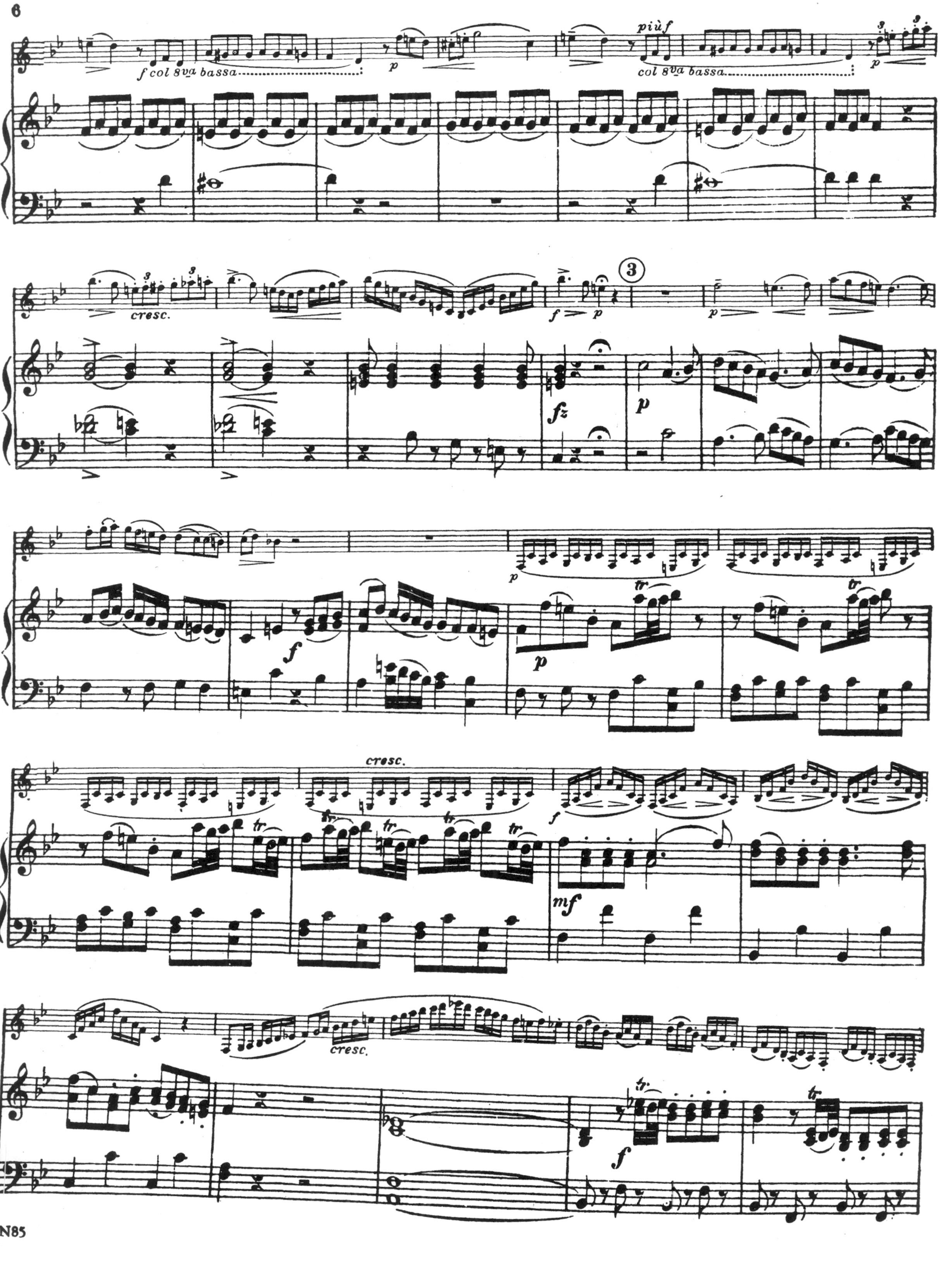
f col 8va bassa
p
più f
col 8va bassa
p
cresc.
f
p
3
p
f
p
f
tr
cresc.
tr
f
mf
cresc.
tr.
f

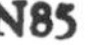

f
cresc.
p
p
f p
cresc.
ff
4
Tutti
f
sempre p
cresc
ff
p
f

5
cresc.
cresc.

6
f
mf
p
p
f
p
fz
p
8fz
cresc.
cresc.
f
7
cresc.
f
8
ff
fp
p
f
f
f

tr
tr
tr
p
f
p
ff
tr

8
Solo
col voce
cresc.
9
cresc.

cresc.
cresc.
10
col 8va bassa
loco
cresc.
col 8va bassa
11
più f
col 8va bassa
cresc.

12
a tempo
p
più f
cresc.
f
fz
mf
tr

p sempre
cresc.
tr
13
cresc.
p

Adagio M.M. 𝅗𝅥=42
p dolce
pp
p
f
A
p
f
B
p
cresc.
p

D
Cadenza by Carl Baermann
Cadenza.
E

Concerto for Clarinet in B♭

(Originally in A Major)

K. 622

WOLFGANG AMADEUS MOZART (1756 –1791)

Revised and Arranged by Simeon Bellison

I.

57
solo
p
63
67
f
tr
71
p
f
tr
75
p
81
cresc.
f
espr.
85
mf
dolce
p
cresc.
90
mf
cresc.
f
95
98
p
103
107
p

cresc.
f espr.
p
p
f
p
più f
p
cresc.
f
p
p
p
cresc.
f
cresc.
f
p
cresc.
f p
sempre p
cresc.
ff

155
159
163
168
172
solo
p
177
p
181
184
cresc.
187
f
f
193
f
p
mf
3

199
f
mf
203
p
f
p
3
208
fz
p
3
cresc.
212
3
3
f
216
fp
f
222
tr
tr
tr
227
232
237

242
246
solo
251
256
261
265
cresc.
269
275
280
cresc.
cresc.
284
cresc.

288
p
292
p
più f
296
p
cresc.
299
espr.
303
p
più f
307
p
312
cresc.
315
a tempo
f
p
320
più f

324
p
cresc.
326
f
329
332
f
335
f
338
p sempre
341
f
345
350
356
II.
Adagio (𝅗𝅥 = 42)
p dolce
8

* Cadenza by Carl Baermann

78
85
mf
pp
p
89
6
mf
pp
espr.
93
p
cresc.
3
f
tr
96
pp
III. Rondo
Allegro (♩. = 88)
p grazioso
4
8
14
19

22 27 31 35 41 47 51 57 62 67 71

poco rit.

a tempo

più f

77
p
82
f
mf
86
p
90
f
p
mf
95
cresc.
f
f
100
p
f
mf
106
p
mf
111
rall.
a tempo
p
f
p
117
p
121
128

136
mf
p
142
fz
fz
mf
148
f
155
f
ff
161
168
f
p
f
p
173
f
177
tr
mf
182
p
cresc.
f
188
p
193
poco rit.
a tempo

197
p
p
203
a tempo
mf
209
212
216
poco rit.
rit.
p
pp
222
a tempo
p
227
p
230
f
p
236
f
mf
p
241
rall.
a tempo
mf
p
f
p
248

252
p
257
p
263
cresc.
266
f
269
p
274
p
278
fz
283
p
287
p
292
f
296
tr

301
p
cresc.
f
p
cresc.
f
f
p
p
cresc.
p
cresc.
f
ff
8va

F
G
H
p
f
mf
pp
espr.
cresc.
tr

Rondo

Allegro M.M. ♩=88

1
fz
p
cresc.
mf
f
p
2
tr

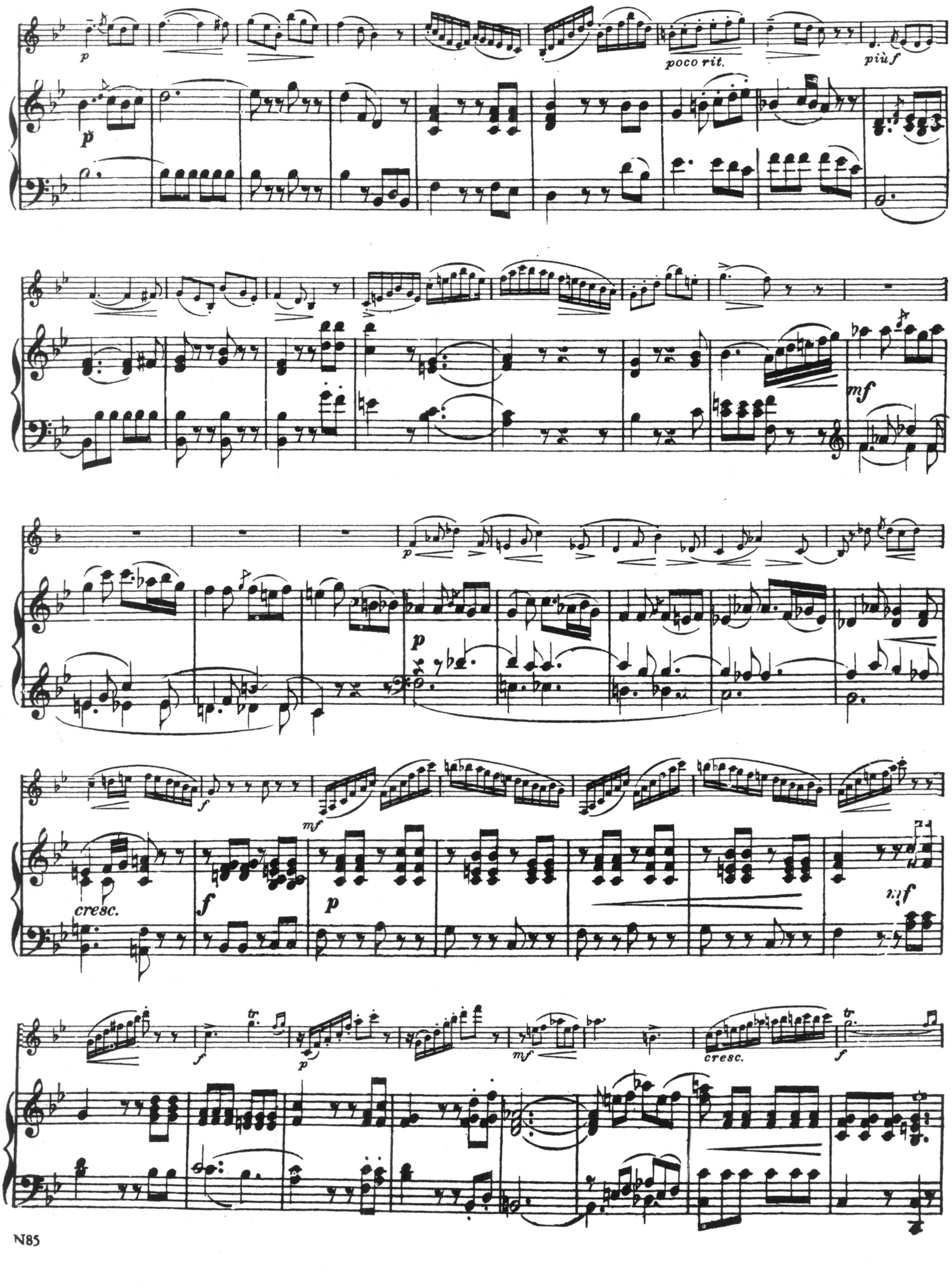
poco rit.
più f
cresc.
mf
cresc.

4
fp
fz
f
p
mf
pp
rall.
5
a tempo
6
ff

p
fz
mf
f
7
ff
fp
8va bassa

8
mf
p
più p
f
p
poco rit.
a tempo
colla voce
9
col 8va bassa
p poco ritard.

pp rit.
10 a tempo
p
a tempo
pp ritard
p
11
p
f
p
fp
fz
f
f
mf
p
p
p
12 a tempo
p
f
rall.
rall.
a tempo
pp
fz
p
p
p
p

13
cresc.
14
cresc.

15
cresc.
cresc.
col 8va bassa
cresc.

16
p
cresc.
cresc.
p
a tempo
cresc.
rit.
p
a tempo
17
cresc.
f
ff
ff

ALBERT
24 Varied Scales & Exercies — O99

ARMATO
Recital Clarinetist — O4862

BAERMANN COMPLETE METHOD (Langenus)
Parts 1 & 2 — O32
Part 3 — O33

BANDMAN'S CLARINET REPERTOIRE
Vol. 2—Concert Music — O4271

CAVALLINI
30 CAPRICES — O106

CLARINET CLASSICS
Volume 1 — CU22
Volume 2 — CU23
Volume 3 — CU24

CLARINETIST'S CONCERT ALBUM — O114

KLOSE-PRESCOTT
First and Second Year — O2575

KROEPSCH
416 Progressive Studies (Bellison)
Book 1—167 Exercises — O312
Book 2—183 Exercises — O313
Book 3—40 Exercises — O314
Book 4—26 Exercises — O315

LANGENUS
Clarinet Repertoire — EMP30
Complete Method:
Part 1 — O1402
Part 2 — O1403
Part 3 — O1404
Practical Transposition — O1405

LAZARUS
Method (Bellison)
Part 1 — O327
Part 2 — O328
Part 3 — O329

LET US HAVE MUSIC FOR CLARINET — O3013

PARES
Daily Exercises & Scales — O773

PEARLS OF THE OLD MASTERS
Volume 1:
Clarinet — CU127
Piano — CU130

REINECKE
Foundation to Clarinet Playing — O221

RODE
20 Studies (Bettoney) — CU236

CLARINET CONCERTOS

MOZART, L.

CONCERTO in Bb Major

_____W2457 (Lillya-Isaac)

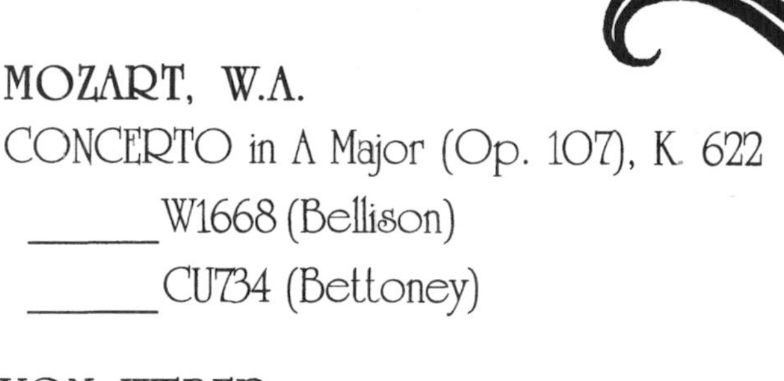

MOZART, W.A.

CONCERTO in A Major (Op. 107), K. 622

_____W1668 (Bellison)

_____CU734 (Bettoney)

VON WEBER

CONCERTO No. 1 in F Minor, Op. 73

_____CU751 (Cundy Bettoney)

_____W1708 (Carl Fischer)

_____CU752 CONCERTO No. 2 in Eb Major, Op. 74

Favorite Solos with Piano Accompaniments on CD

The Carl Fischer CD Solo Series is designed to help all levels of instrumental soloists improve their performances by making practice time more productive with the included "live" piano accompaniment.

The CD contains a beautifully recorded piano accompaniment performed by Melody Lord who has years of experience accompanying soloist of all ability levels.

The CD Solo Series is an invaluable teaching tool and is presented in 3 graded levels: Beginning (Gr. 2), Intermediate (Gr. 3) and Advanced (Gr. 4-5).

As an added bonus, the faster pieces in the Beginning Level have a second track with the piano accompaniment at a rehearsal tempo to assist in the preparation of the piece.

Works for Clarinet and Piano

In the Carl Fischer CD Solo Series

Beginning level

W2624	Arioso — Largo from *Concerto for Harpsichord and String Orchestra*	Johann Sebastian Bach
W2628	Gigue	Arcangelo Corelli
W2629	Gymnopédie No. 2 from *Trois Gymnopédies*	Erik Satie
W2630	Musical Moment from *6 Moments Musicaux*	Franz Schubert
W2579	Tambourin	François Joseph Gossec
W2627	Träumerei from *Scenes from Childhood* ("Kinderscenen")	Robert Schumann

Intermediate Level

W2582	Allegretto	Benjamin Godard, Op. 116, No. 1
W2584	Berceuse	Gabriel Fauré, Op. 16
W2583	Entr'acte from *Carmen*	Georges Bizet
W2581	Giga from *Sonata in F Major*	George Frideric Handel, Op. 1, No. 1
W2585	Sicilienne from *Pelléas et Mélisande*	Gabriel Fauré
W2625	Siciliano from *Sonata No. 2 in E♭ Major*	Johann Sebastian Bach
W2626	Sonata in F Major	Benedetto Marcello

Advanced Level

W2586	Concertino	Carl Maria von Weber, Op. 26
W2587	Concerto No. 1 in F minor for B♭ Clarinet and Piano	Carl Maria von Weber, Op. 73
W2588	Grand Duo Concertant	Carl Maria von Weber, Op. 120, No. 1
W2632	Introduction, Theme and Variations from *Sehnsuchts-Walzer* by Franz Schubert	Ferdinand David
W2590	Sonata in E♭ Major, Op. 120, No. 2	Johannes Brahms, Op. 120, No. 2
W2589	Sonata in F minor for Clarinet and Piano	Johannes Brahms, Op. 120, No. 1
W2631	Theme and Variations Fourth Movement from *Quintet for Clarinet and Strings*	Wolfgang Amadeus Mozart, K. 581